It was Monday.

Mum, Joe and Kate were at home.

Mum was cleaning the house.

She looked out of the window.

'I can see the postman,' said Mum.

'I want to see him too,' said Joe.

'I can see a police car,' said Mum.

'I want to see it too,'
said Joe.

'I can see a bus,'
said Mum.

'I want to see it too,'
said Joe.

'I can see a tractor,'
said Mum.

'I want to see it too,'
said Joe.

'I can see the tractor!'
said Joe.